USBORNE
1001
Knights
and Castle
Things to spot

Hazel Maskell

Illustrated and designed by
Teri Gower

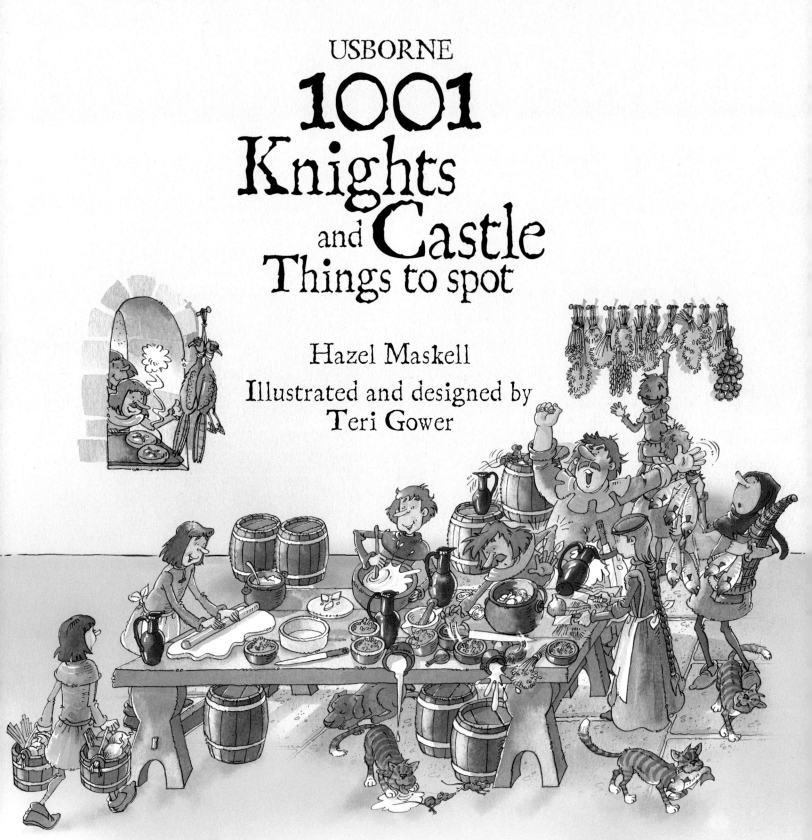

Additional design by Nelupa Hussain
Edited by Anna Milbourne
History consultant: Dr. Abigail Wheatley

Contents

Things to spot

Long ago, knights lived in castles and spent their time riding off on thrilling adventures. Take a trip into their world, where each of the scenes is filled with all kinds of exciting things for you to find and count. There are 1001 things to spot altogether.

Castle life

3 washing tubs

8 metal tongs

10 pitchforks

1 Lord Robert

9 buckets of water

4 messengers

10 hens

9 bundles of straw

5 saws

7 spotted puppies

7

Each little picture shows you what to look for in the big picture.

The number tells you how many of that thing you need to find.

This is Will, a squire at the castle. See if you can spot him in each big scene, then help him with his quest to become a knight on page 30.

A castle home

10 castle guards

8 ravens

7 pennants

10 black sheep

5 cottages

9 knights on horses

1 castle keep

6 fishermen

5 carts of hay

4

2 portcullises

Castle life

9 buckets of water

3 washing tubs

8 metal tongs

10 pitchforks

1 Lord Robert

4 messengers

10 hens

9 bundles of straw

5 saws

7 spotted puppies

In the kitchen

8 fish

10 brown mice

6 kitchen cats

9 loaves of bread

5 pots of hot soup

9 red jugs

7 barrels

6 bowls of herbs

5 kitchen knives

8 roasting chickens

A village fair

8 stinky cheeses

9 pewter plates

3 pickpockets

6 horse brushes

10 new boots

7 pots of honey

4 knight puppets

9 gold coins

8 geese

10 vials of love potion

Woodland rescue

1 red knight

8 hunting horns

10 barking hounds

2 damsels in distress

4 white stags

9 crows cawing

6 galloping horses

9 spears

10 wild boar piglets

7 quivers of arrows

Fantastic feast

 1 harp

 9 lit candles

 7 flower salads

8 roast pheasants

 2 jesters

10 knives

9 jugs with faces

8 steaming pies

3 stuffed swans

8 honey
cakes

Winter party

7 sleds

10 hot drinks

9 flaming torches

5 howling wolves

8 bunches of holly

7 baskets of firewood

8 snow knights

6 red hoods

9 mince pies

10 snowballs

Spring tournament

2 heralds 9 bows 7 striped pavilions 8 wreaths 10 arrows

9 crows cawing

6 galloping horses

9 spears

10 wild boar piglets

7 quivers of arrows

13

Fantastic feast

1 harp

9 lit candles

7 flower salads

8 roast pheasants

2 jesters

10 knives

9 jugs with faces

8 steaming pies

3 stuffed swans

8 helmets with plumes

6 lucky green gloves

5 pie-sellers

4 injured knights

10 broken lances

May Day

8 May trees

8 hobby horses

7 acrobats

8 drums

10 spinning tops

1 May queen

1 May pole

4 bagpipes

10 leafy crowns

10 skittles

Castle garden

 **10** flower garlands

 **3** chess boards

 **9** cooing doves

 10 red roses

 **7** lutes

10 golden pears

9 baskets

4 books

1 splashing fountain

8 pet dogs

Knight school

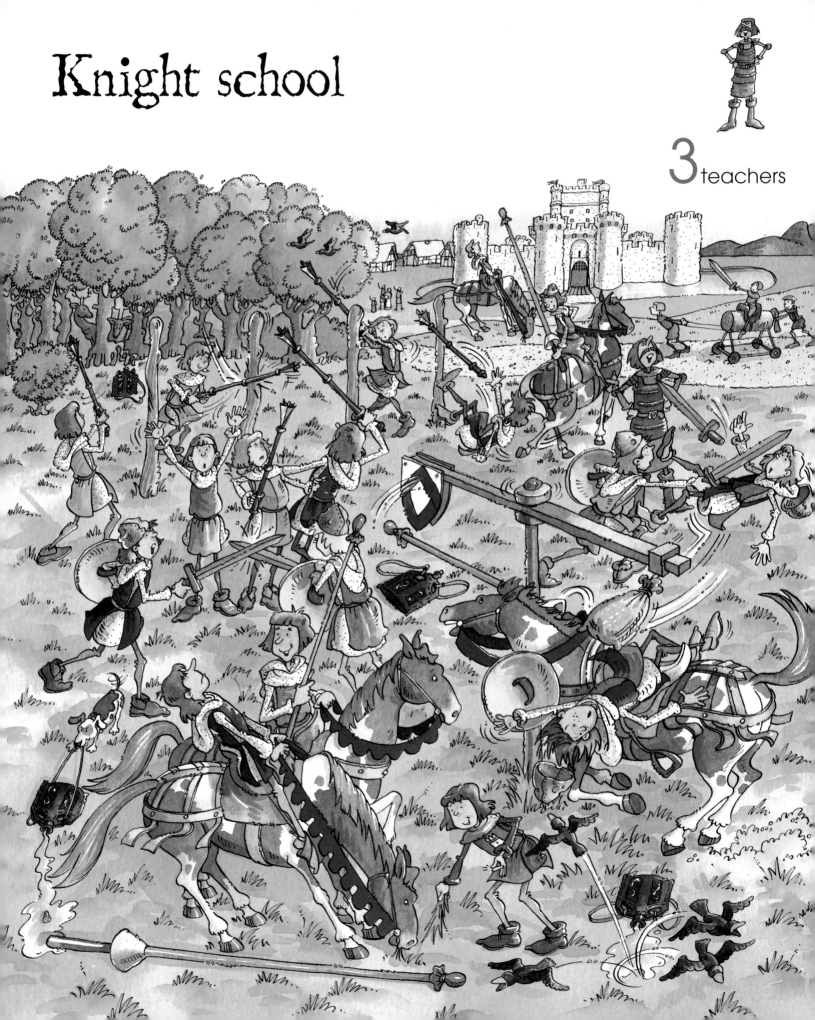

3 teachers

5 attack poles

10 wooden swords

9 round shields

3 quintains

4 squires tumbling

8 blackbirds

7 maces

10 battered helmets

9 ponies

Knights at arms

10 boulders

1 siege tower

3 catapults

10 shovels

7 army pavilions

5 giant shields

9 flaming arrows

4 knights swimming

7 ladders

1 battering ram

27

New knights

7 love tokens

10 metal gauntlets

3 priests

9 swords in sheaths

8 new helmets

8 trays of food

5 trumpets

9 ruby rings

7 blue flags

10 golden spurs

Squire's quest

Will desperately wants to become a knight, but first he must prove himself worthy. To test him, Lord Robert has sent him on a quest to find all these objects. Look back through the book and see if you can help Will to spot them all.

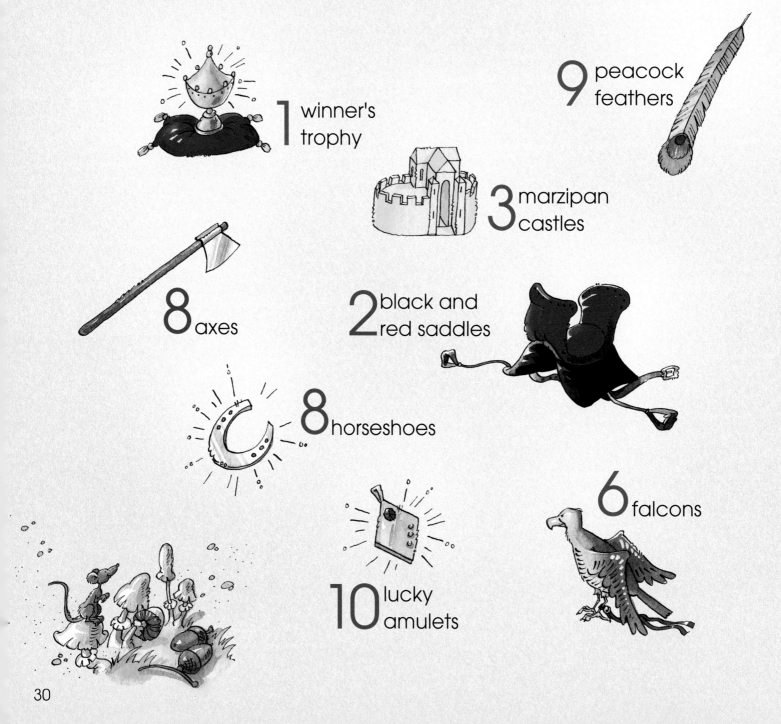

1 winner's trophy

9 peacock feathers

3 marzipan castles

8 axes

2 black and red saddles

8 horseshoes

10 lucky amulets

6 falcons

2 white horses

10 water bottles

7 golden goblets

1 jewel-encrusted sword

9 serpent shields

10 stolen necklaces

8 masks with antlers

Answers

Did you help Will to spot everything on his list?
Here's where they all are:

1 winner's trophy
Spring tournament
(pages 18-19)

8 axes
Winter party
(pages 16-17)

8 horseshoes
Castle life
(pages 6-7)

2 black and red saddles
Castle life
(pages 6-7)

10 lucky amulets
A village fair
(pages 10-11)

9 peacock feathers
In the kitchen
(pages 8-9)

3 marzipan castles
Fantastic feast
(pages 14-15)

6 falcons
Castle garden
(pages 22-23)

2 white horses
A castle home
(pages 4-5)

10 water bottles
Knight school
(pages 24-25)

7 golden goblets
Fantastic feast
(pages 14-15)

1 jewel-encrusted sword
New knights
(pages 28-29)

10 stolen necklaces
Woodland rescue
(pages 12-13)

8 masks with antlers
May Day
(pages 20-21)

9 serpent shields
Knights at arms
(pages 26-27)

First published in 2010 by Usborne Publishing Ltd.,
Usborne House, 83-85 Saffron Hill, London EC1N 8RT, England. www.usborne.co.uk
Copyright © 2010, Usborne Publishing Ltd. The name Usborne and the devices 🖋⬮ are Trade Marks of Usborne Publishing Ltd.
First published in America in 2010. UE. Printed in China.